All you need to 'see' the 3D illusions are your eyes and some patience. To discover your MAGIC EYE, focus your eyes as if you're looking at a distant object.

Method One

Hold the image so that it touches your nose. Let the eyes relax, and stare vacantly off into space, as if looking through the image. Relax and become comfortable with the idea of observing the image, without looking at it. When you are relaxed and not crossing your eyes, move the page slowly away from your face. Perhaps an inch every two or three seconds. Keep looking through the page. Stop at a comfortable reading distance and keep staring. The most discipline is needed when something starts to 'come in', because at that moment you'll instinctively try to look at the page rather than looking through it. If you look at it, start again.

Method Two

The cover of this book is shiny; hold it in such a way that you can identify a reflection. For example, hold it under an overhead lamp so that it catches its light. Simply look at the object you see reflected, and continue to stare at it with a fixed gaze. After several seconds, you'll perceive depth, followed by the 3D image, which will develop almost like an instant photo!

3D Images by N.E. Thing Enterprises

MAGIC EYE
MAGIC NOSE

Magicked up by Comic Relief

Michael Joseph

London

MICHAEL JOSEPH LTD

Published by the Penguin Group
27 Wrights Lane, London W8 5TZ
Viking Penguin Inc., 375 Hudson Street, New York, New York 10014, USA
Penguin Books Australia Ltd, Ringwood, Victoria, Australia
Penguin Books Canada Ltd, 10 Alcorn Avenue, Toronto, Ontario, Canada M4V 3B2
Penguin Books (NZ) Ltd, 182-190 Wairau Road, Auckland 10, New Zealand

Penguin Books Ltd, Registered Offices: Harmondsworth, Middlesex, England

First published in Great Britain 1995

Copyright © N.E. Thing Enterprises Ltd and Comic Relief Ltd 1995

Colour reproduction by Saxon, Norwich
Book interior designed by Design/Section, Frome
Printed and bound in Great Britain by Butler & Tanner Ltd, Frome and London

ISBN 0 7181 3963 1

The moral right of the author has been asserted

MAGIC EYE and WIZZY NODWIG are trademarks of N.E. Thing Enterprises Inc

INTRODUCTION

Well, here's the thing.

There's this dude called Tom Baccei who's the Big Wig and Big Beard at N.E. Thing Enterprises and we heard he was coming to England. So we decided we weren't going to let him out of the country without him agreeing to help Comic Relief produce the ultimate Magic Eye 3D book.

Our plan was cunning and very cruel. As you know, these fabulous Magic Eye books have earned a fortune by making people look at slightly confusing images – out of which emerges a second, at first ghostly, then glorious image – and sometimes even a third. But the thing is, when you first try, it's sometimes a little wearing on the eye.

Well, we decided to give Tom a piece of his own medicine. We tracked him down and then forced him to sit in a chair, and look for a long time *at a picture of Chris Evans*. And here's the horror: even though Tom stared and stared at it, it never changed!! *There was no second image*!!! All Tom could do was take in the full horror; white skin, bright stupid orange hair, glasses of which even Eric Morecambe would have been ashamed.

After about ten minutes, he was a deeply depressed man. After five minutes looking at a picture of Jonathan Ross arm-in-arm with Danny Baker and Terry Wogan, he was physically unwell. After a terrible thirty-second encounter with a close-up photograph of Ken Dodd, he had signed on the dotted line to produce the wonderful book your eyes are about to dive into and swim about in.

It's a fantastic pot-pourri of caylyptosramptious, kaleidospheric, snozzical, slaptickling and grabulous images. Some of them are riddles with the answers revealed in the third dimension – some of them are limericks – some of them are oulyrageous and, let's be frank, distinctly wibby geometrical conundrums.

All of them are magical and more than wondiferous and we hope will give you a positively slaptickling time. Massive thanks to everyone at N.E. Thing who worked right through Thanksgiving without so much as a nosular whiff of turkey to produce this book, everyone at Michael Joseph, particularly Susan Watt-Do-You-Mean-It's-Not-Finished-Yet and all the suppliers and distributors who've helped make sure a good chunk of your cash goes straight to Comic Relief and its tremungous projects.

And of course, thanks to you for buying it and supporting us. Now read on – and give your eyes the kind of massage that has been illegal in all civilized countries for the last 100 years.

Lenny Henry

Trustee, Comic Relief and the Cool-Looking Guy on the Front of this Book

P.S. Just to get you going: the first fabulousness opposite tells you exactly what you ought to do when someone chucks a rotten tomato at you.

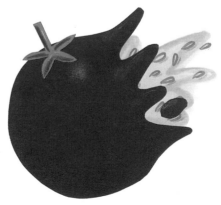

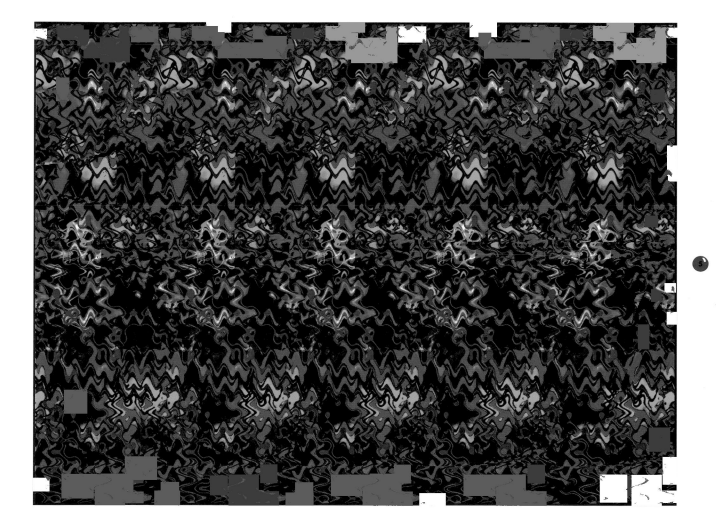

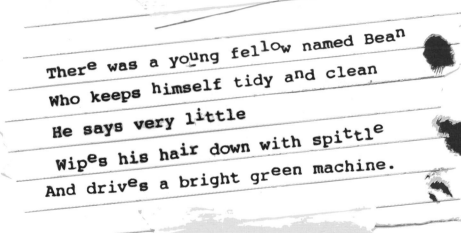

There was a young fellow named Bean
Who keeps himself tidy and clean
He says very little
Wipes his hair down with spittle
And drives a bright green machine.

THREE CRUCIAL COMIC RELIEF QUESTIONS

1 How much of the money you give on Red Nose Day goes to pay Comic Relief fundraising costs?

2 How many good reasons are there why there should be discrimination against people with disabilities?

3 How many people in the U.K. live more than fifty miles away from a project Comic Relief supports?

The answers are in the picture opposite.

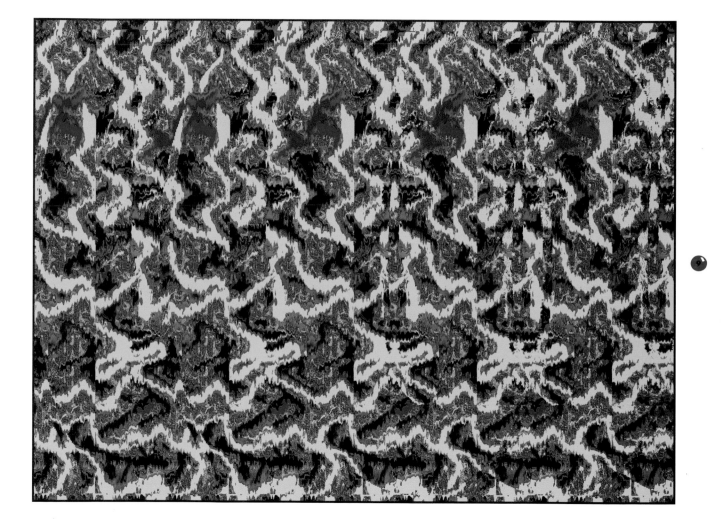

What do you get if you cross a kangaroo with a sheep?

 In 1993, Mr H. Simmonds of Abingdon chaired a board meeting in a rabbit costume. Of the money he raised, fifty pounds will cover the costs of a vaccine gun used in Mozambique.

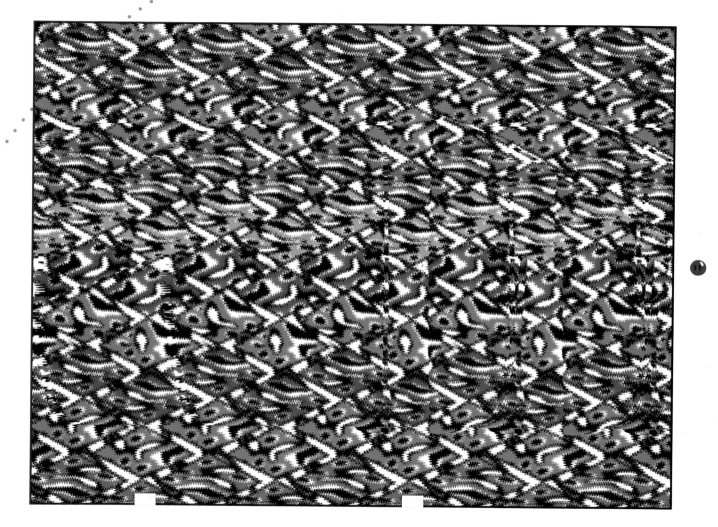

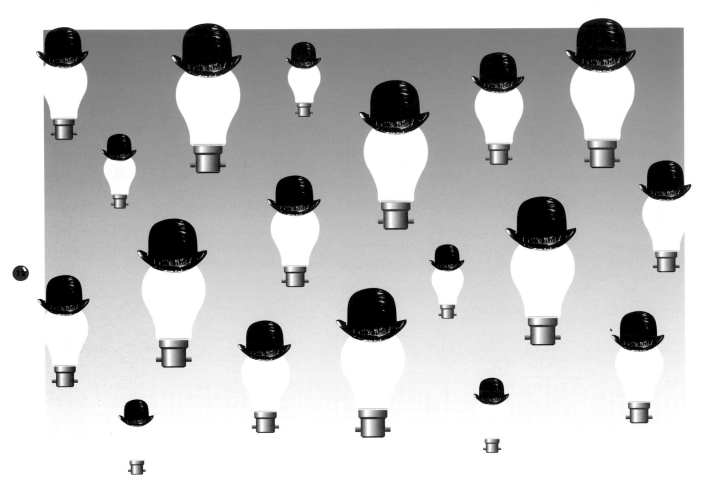

How many surrealists does it take to change a lightbulb?

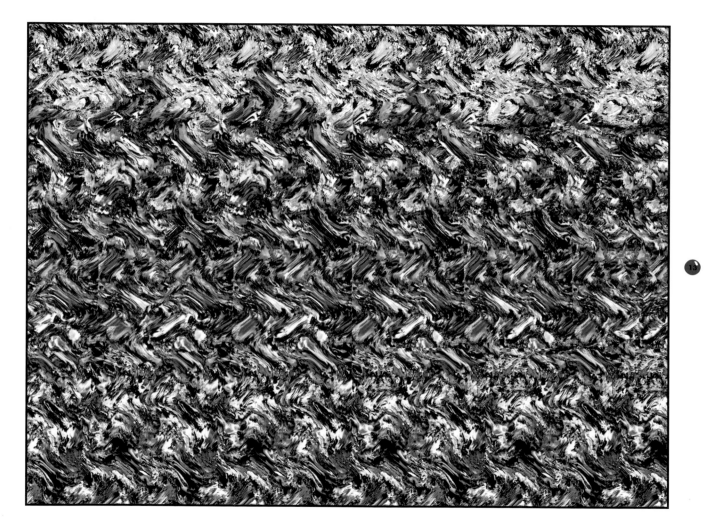

One called Laurie, the other called Fry

One very tall, the other quite high.

Both very polite

When rude, both contrite,

And they sport these when sporting black tie.

———————

14

 During Red Nose Day 4, 138,476 separate fund-raising events took place for us throughout the U.K. Some of our favourites included the sponsored underwater dinner party, the seven-year-old boy with chicken pox who was sponsored per spot, and the many pregnant women who went into sponsored labour.

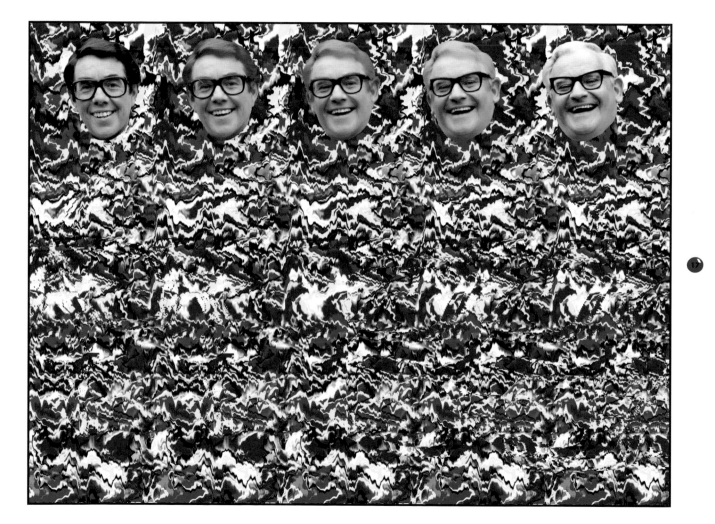

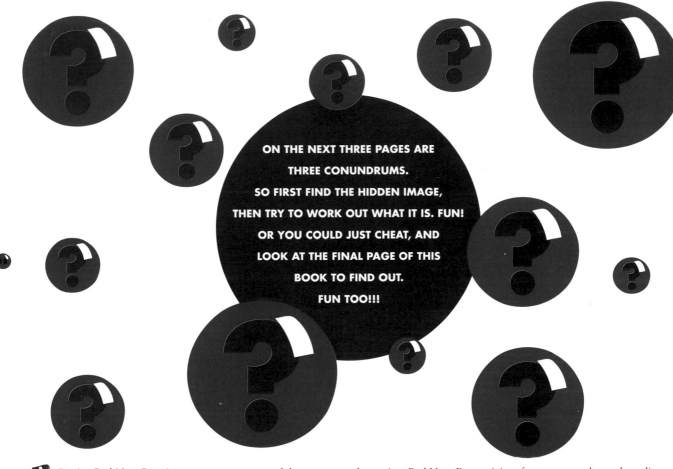

ON THE NEXT THREE PAGES ARE
THREE CONUNDRUMS.
SO FIRST FIND THE HIDDEN IMAGE,
THEN TRY TO WORK OUT WHAT IT IS. FUN!
OR YOU COULD JUST CHEAT, AND
LOOK AT THE FINAL PAGE OF THIS
BOOK TO FIND OUT.
FUN TOO!!!

 During Red Nose Day 4, seventy-two per cent of the country took part in a Red Nose Day activity of some sort and our phone lines registered 4.1 million attempted calls – and we raised £18,000,000.

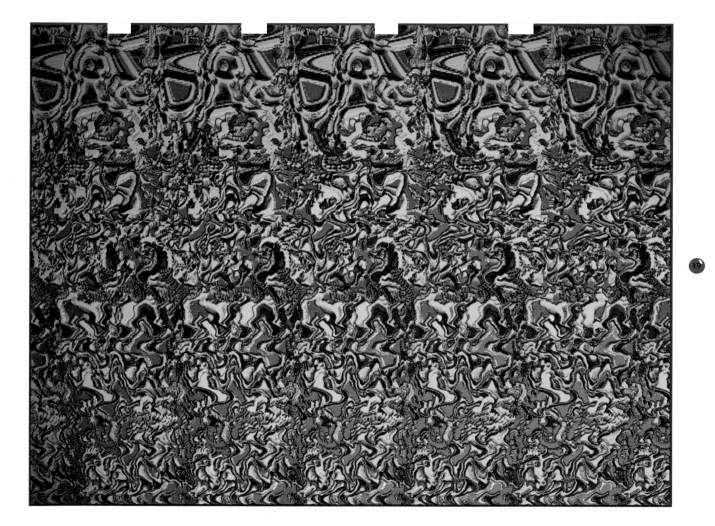

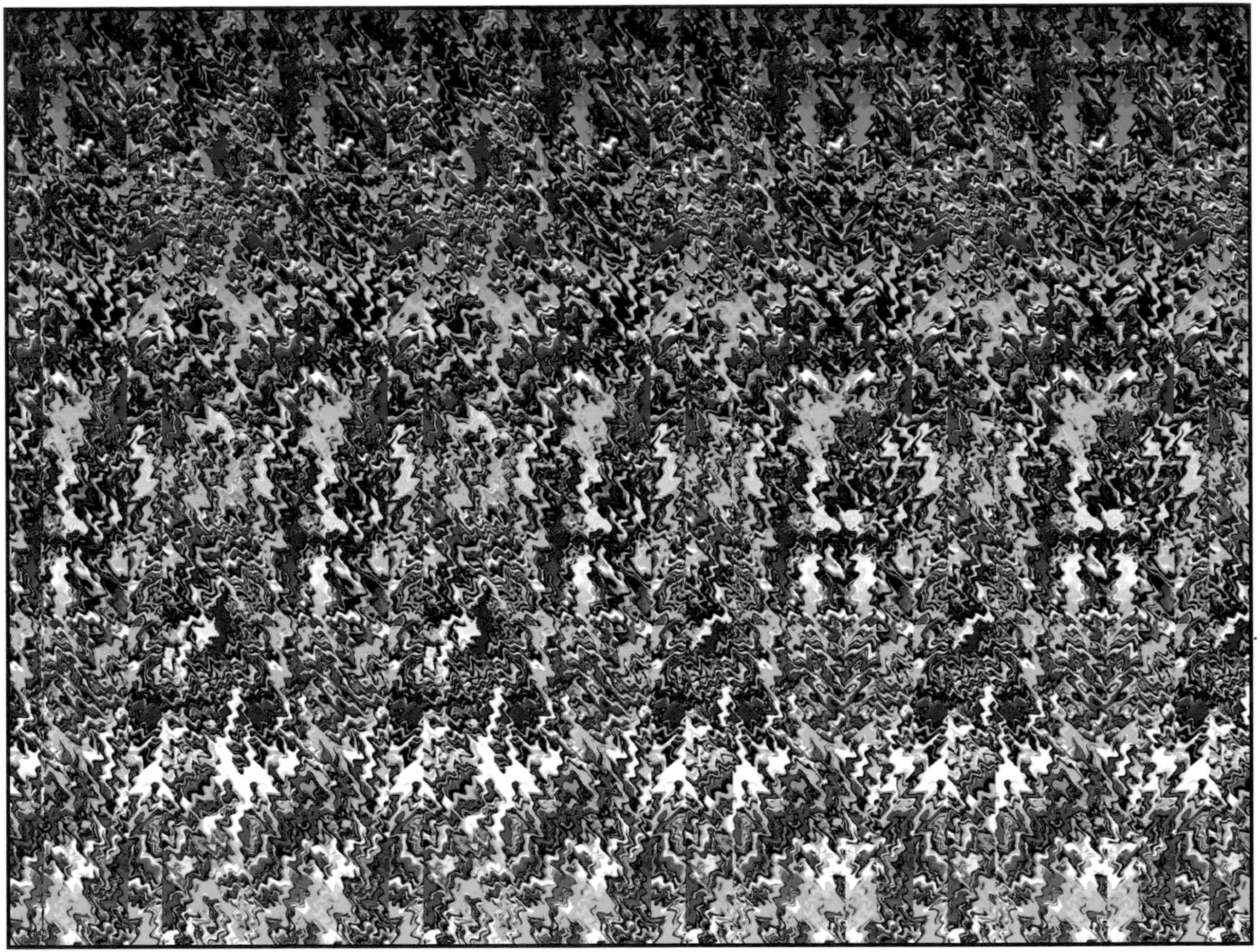

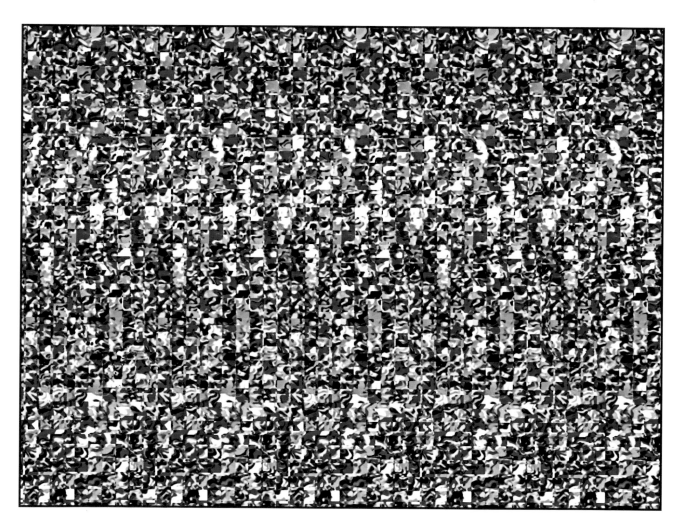

Why can't you play cards in the jungle?

In buying this book, you're giving directly to people in Africa. As little as ten pence can buy a life-saving sachet of oral dehydration salts - the most effective means of combating diarrhoea.

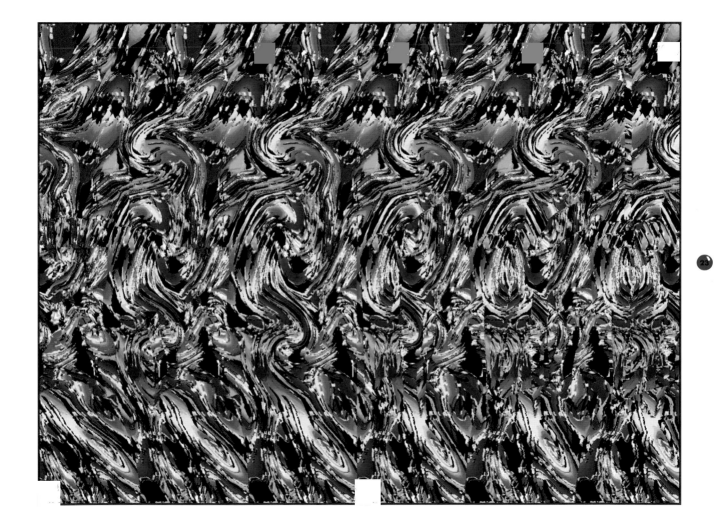

Young Chris has got his eyes peeled
For the image so subtly concealed
If you look and calm down
Off that brow wipe your frown
You will see the secret revealed

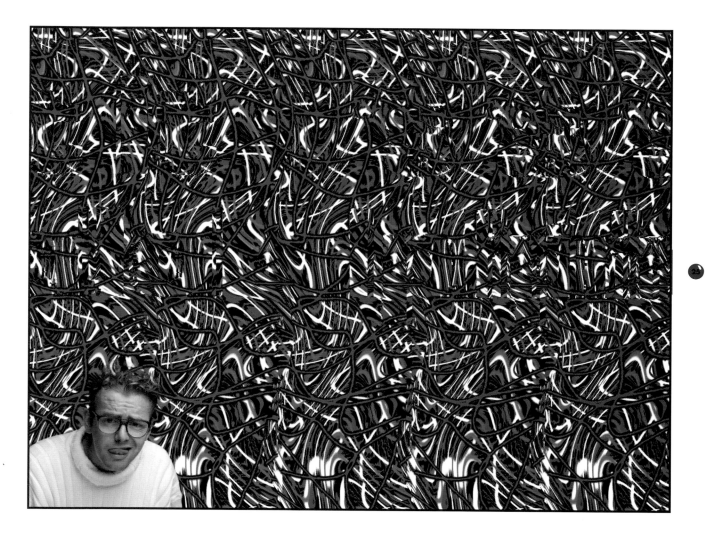

There are two chaps called
Gazza and Platt

And football they're geniuses at

Red cards they hate

But they don't hesitate

To put on red noses and chat

One third of all Comic Relief money is spent in the U.K. – that's over £31,000,000 so far. Somewhere round the corner from you, Comic Relief is giving older people and disabled people more choices and providing crucial help to young people who are homeless or in trouble with drugs or alcohol.

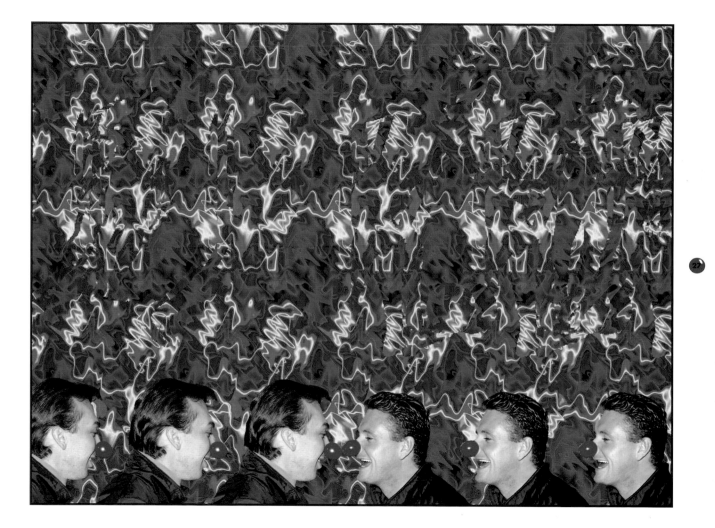

WHAT DID RAY TURN INTO WHEN HE GOT STEPPED ON BY AN ELEPHANT?

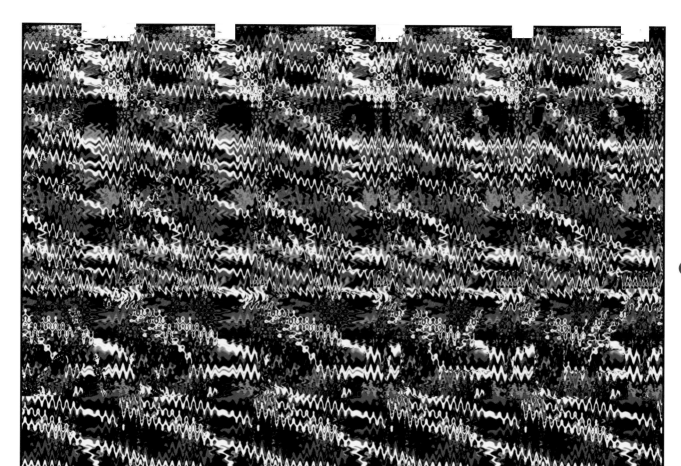

When dressed in the clothes of their choix

These ladies wear only Lacroix

One called Patsy

The other, more fatsy,

Go together like well-podded pois

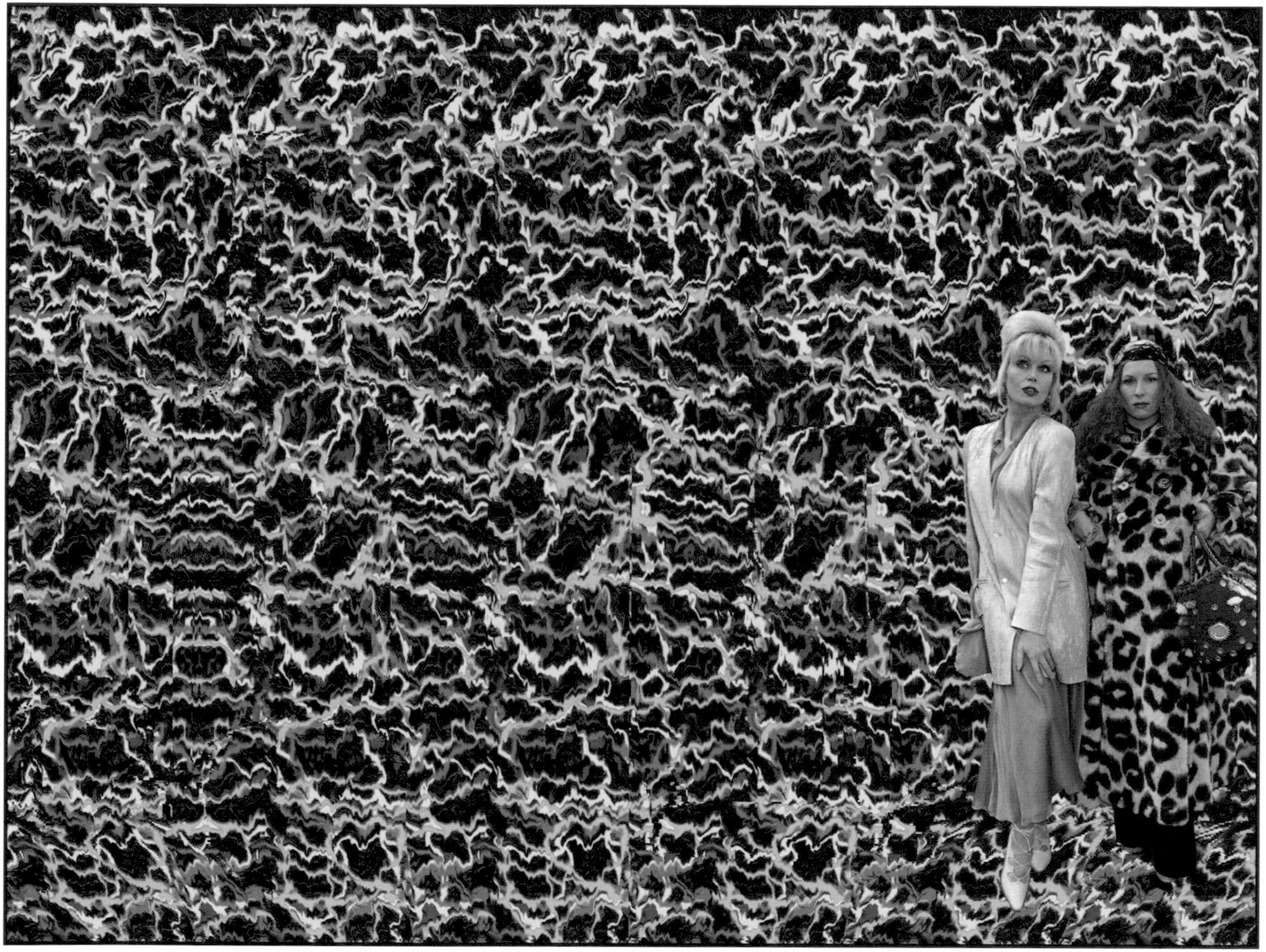

**On the next three pages are three X-Rated Conundrums.
If you are over eighteen, find the hidden image and then try to work out what it is.
If you are under eighteen, find the hidden image, but then forget all about it and move on please.**

 Measles, polio, diphtheria, whooping cough, tuberculosis and tetanus are the six main childhood killers in Africa. Three pounds will pay for the immunisation of a child against all these diseases.

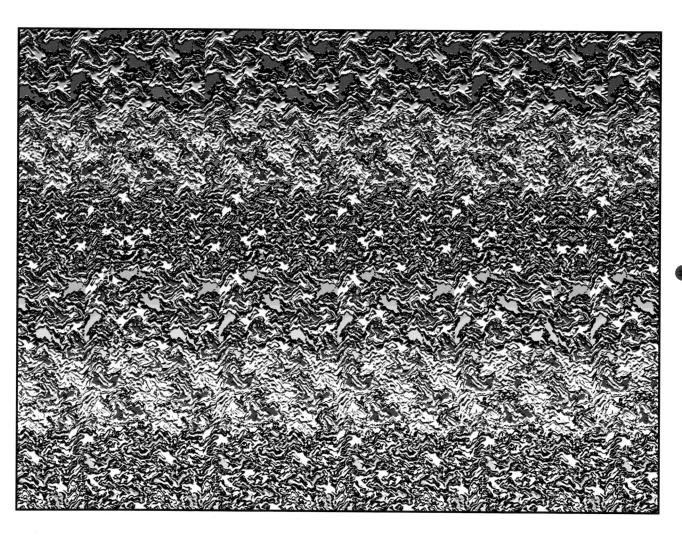

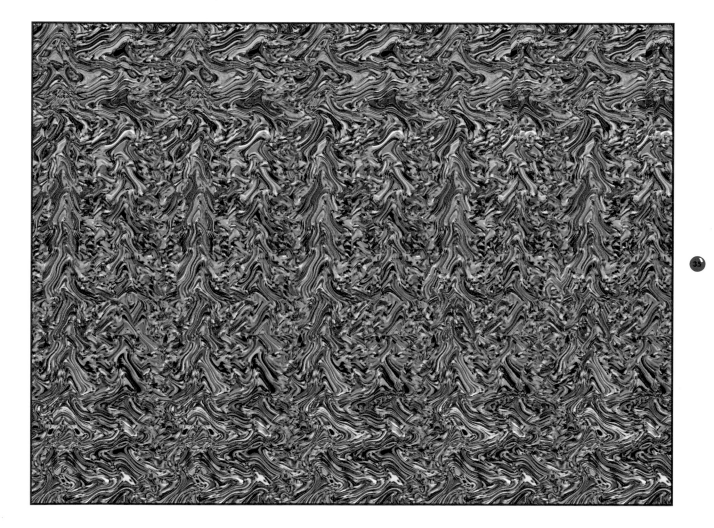

35

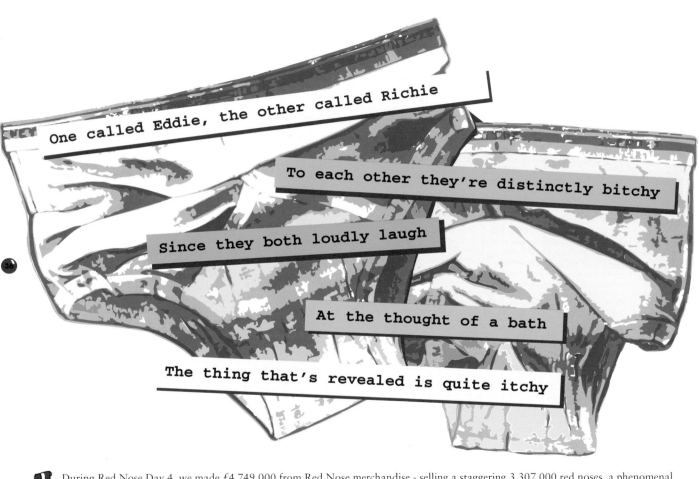

One called Eddie, the other called Richie

To each other they're distinctly bitchy

Since they both loudly laugh

At the thought of a bath

The thing that's revealed is quite itchy

During Red Nose Day 4, we made £4,749,000 from Red Nose merchandise - selling a staggering 3,307,000 red noses, a phenomenal 650,000 car and truck noses, and an unexpected 250,000 T-shirts. We also managed to sell six Red Nose loo seat covers. These were not considered a success.

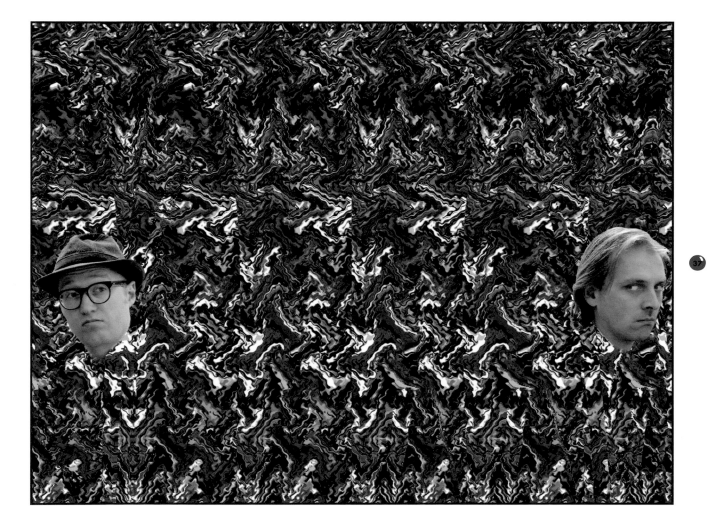

What's orange and sounds like a parrot?

What's orange and sounds like a parrot?

What's orange and sounds like a parrot?

What's orange and sounds like a parrot?

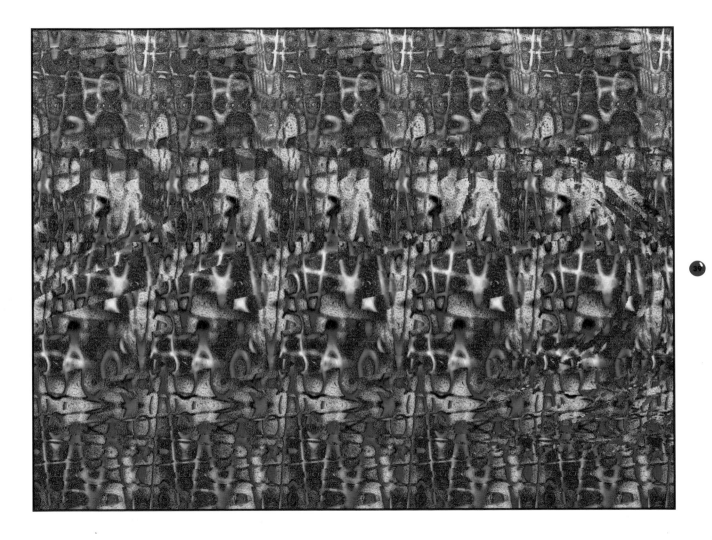

What do you call it when insects run away and get married?

 Malaria is still one of the biggest killer diseases in Africa. A tiny twenty pence can buy medicine needed to treat a child suffering from a potentially fatal attack.

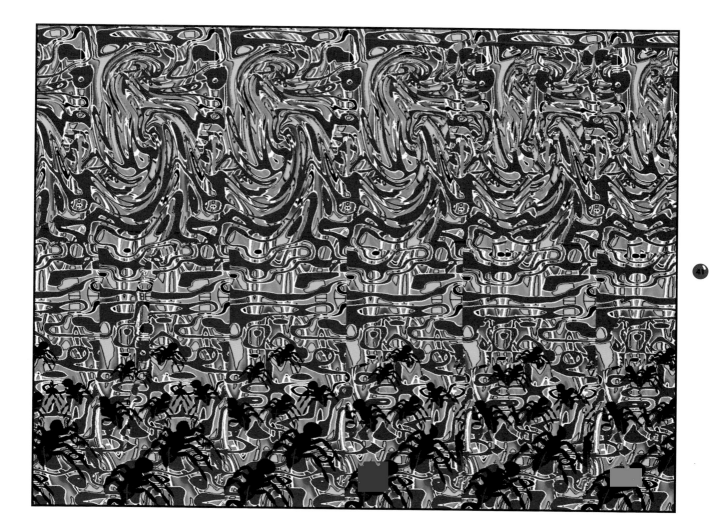

What do you get if you put a poodle on a radiator?

This darling young man called Hugh'd

Found his looks had been highly reviewed

If you screw your eyes tight

At the page on the right

You will see him stark raving nude

5 A duck

7 Another kind of Bean

9 The answer to all three questions

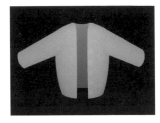

11 A woolly jumper

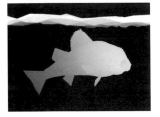

13 A fish

15 Elegant monocle and cigarette

17 Two pairs of iconic spectacles

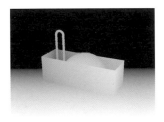

19 New-born trombonist

20 Baby bear climbing tree with frozen snake in its mouth

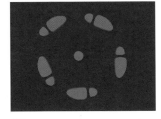

21 Long John Silver with leg stuck in bung-hole

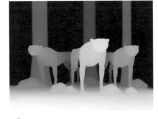

23 Too many cheetahs

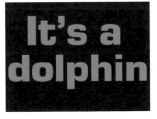

25 Don't forget your dolphin

27 Dream footballers

29 An X-ray

31 Patsy's regular diet

33 What you get when you cross Madonna with a bowling ball

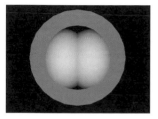

35 Water's eye view before the impending splash

35 Two bunjee jumpers about to have sex

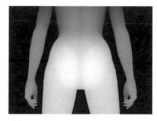

37 A rather nice bottom

39 A carrot

41 An antelope

43 A hot-dog

45 An awful cheat

ACKNOWLEDGEMENTS

Thanks are due to many people for so much help, freely and willingly given, under considerable time pressure.

Firstly to Tom Baccei and his team at N.E. Thing Enterprises, not only for the great Magic Eye images, but for the wholehearted way they joined in the enterprise, even working holidays and weekends.

To photographers, Stephen Morley, John Green, Eric Tessier, John Jefford, Steve Shipman, Trevor Leighton, Chris Harrow, Mark Harrison, who allowed us to use their photographs without payment.

To Rowan Atkinson, Ronnie Barker, Ronnie Corbett, Ade Edmondson, Chris Evans, Dawn French, Stephen Fry, Paul Gascoigne, Hugh Grant, Lenny Henry, Hugh Laurie, Joanna Lumley, Rik Mayall, David Platt, Jonathan Ross and Jennifer Saunders for allowing their names and faces to be taken in vain.

To Graham Webb, Pippa Martin and Caroline Wilson at Design/Section for all their hard work on the text design.

To Butler & Tanner for their generous gift to Comic Relief and for printing the book in no time at all.

To Smurfit Townsend Hook Ltd for giving paper to Comic Relief and to Saxon Colour Repro Ltd for their kind donation.

And to all you readers for the donations you are making to Comic Relief.

It really makes a difference.